Fly through Reception Phonics with CGP!

CGP's Targeted Practice Books are packed with fun and friendly activities to build Reception pupils' confidence as they start to read and write.

What's more, they follow the National Curriculum 'Letters and Sounds' programme, so you can be sure they cover everything children need to learn.

This is **Reception Targeted Practice Book 5**. It covers **Phase 4** of the 'Letters and Sounds' programme, including:

- **Adjacent consonants** such as **cr**, **sk**, **st**, **nd**, **lt** and **nch**
- More **tricky words**

What CGP is all about

Our sole aim here at CGP is to produce the highest quality books — carefully written, immaculately presented and dangerously close to being funny.

Then we work our socks off to get them out to you — at the cheapest possible prices.

How to Use this Book

In this Book

You'll meet...

 **Jolly Jugglers**: they'll help you practise those tricky words

 Word Birds: they'll help you read and write words and sentences

Hints for Helpers

Here are a few things to bear in mind when using this book:

- CGP's Phonics series aligns with **Letters and Sounds**, the Department for Education's systematic synthetic phonics programme. Books 1-4 cover Phases 1, 2 and 3. This book focuses on Phase 4.

- The book should be worked through **in order**, as new content builds on content covered earlier in the book.

- Some page titles in this book refer to, for example, 'CVCC' words. 'C' is for consonant and 'V' is for vowel — so 'mist' would be an example of a CVCC word.

- A grey line under two or more letters in a word is a reminder that these letters work together to make one sound. It's a helpful prompt when blending sounds to read words.

  thrill

- 'Tricky words' are words with letters that have a sound that does not correspond to the expected sound, or that have a sound that has not yet been learned. These words need to be practised until they can be read straight away without blending sounds.

- 'Word frames' and 'letter cards' are used in spelling and writing activities. The word frames have one box for each sound in the word. The letter or letters for that sound are shown on letter cards. The letters can be copied into the word frame boxes.

- This resource requires children to match images to words. You may need to help children to **identify** some images they're not sure of.

Above all, promote a **positive, confident attitude** towards reading and writing by giving lots of praise and encouragement.

Contents

Written by Karen Bryant-Mole

Editors: Laura Collins, Christopher Lindle, Sam Norman, Jack Tooth
Reviewers: Ross Knaggs, Clare Leck, Lucy Towle
With thanks to Zoe Fenwick and Anne James for the proofreading.
ISBN: 978 1 78908 015 5

Images throughout the book from www.edu-clips.com
Printed by Elanders Ltd, Newcastle upon Tyne.
Based on the classic CGP style created by Richard Parsons.

Book 4 Check

Look at each card in turn. Say the sound.
Match the card to something that has that sound in it.

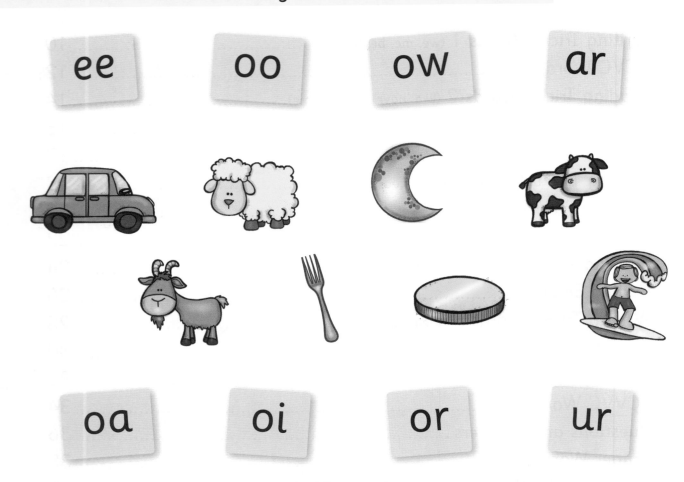

ee   oo   ow   ar

oa   oi   or   ur

Read the captions under each picture.
Circle the correct caption.

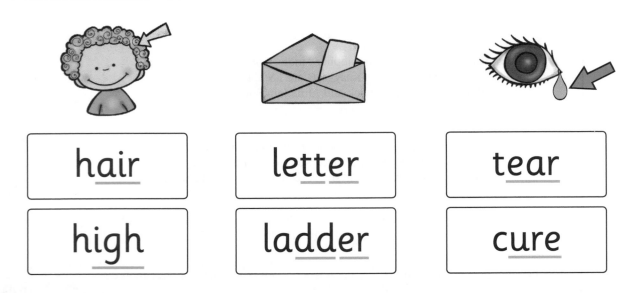

| hair | letter | tear |
| high | ladder | cure |

Do you know these tricky words?
Colour the juggling ball below each tricky word you can read.

was my you

they her all are

Say the words **tail** and **feet**. **Find** the letters. **Write** the words.

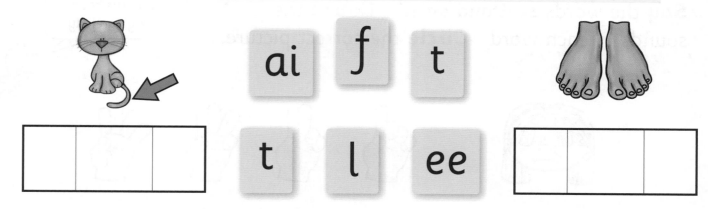

ai f t

t l ee

Say: I go along. Write this sentence in the word frames.

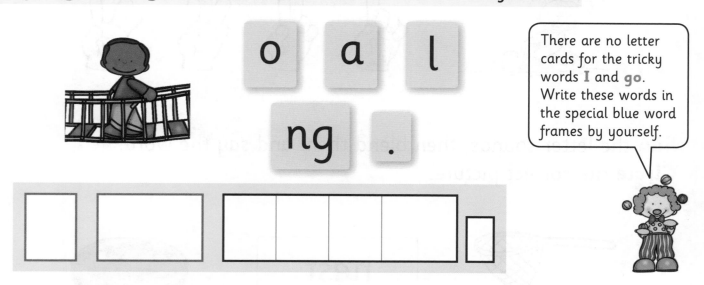

o a l

ng .

There are no letter cards for the tricky words **I** and **go**. Write these words in the special blue word frames by yourself.

I can remember everything I learned in Book 4.

Phonics — Reception Book 5

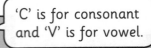

'C' is for consonant and 'V' is for vowel.

CVCC Words

Say the sounds in the word cap.
Now, say the sounds in the word camp.

Can you hear?
There are three sounds in cap: c - a - p.

There are four sounds in camp: c - a - m - p.

Say the words **sad** and **sand**. **Count** the
sounds in each word. **Circle** the correct picture.

Say the sounds very carefully.

Say the letter sounds, then blend them and say the word.
Circle the correct picture.

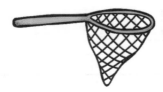

nest

Read each caption. **Match** it to the correct picture.

desk

belt

Say the words **wind** and **chest**. **Say** the sounds in each word.
Write the letters in the word frames.

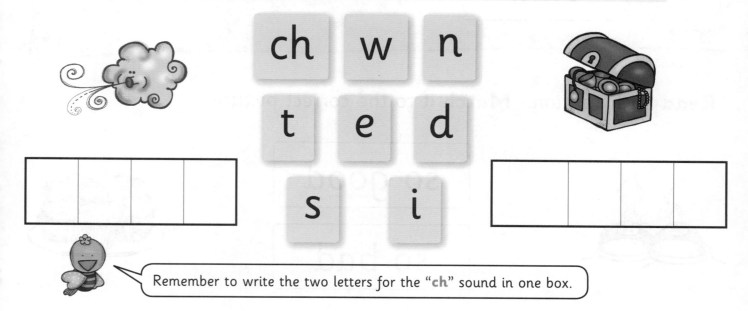

Remember to write the two letters for the "**ch**" sound in one box.

Read the sentence. **Circle** the best picture for the sentence.

Wilf and Ant went to the pond.

I can read and write words that have two
consonants next to each other at the end.

Reading Tricky Words 1

Remember! Some of the letters in tricky words have sounds you don't expect. The tricky words here are **so** and **said**.

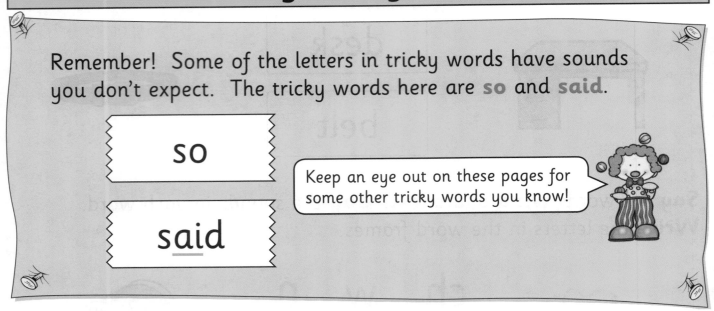

so

said

Keep an eye out on these pages for some other tricky words you know!

Read each caption. **Match** it to the correct picture.

so good

so bad

Look at the picture. **Read** the sentences.
Circle the sentence that makes sense.

She said a song.

She sang a song.

You need to practise tricky words until you can read them straight away.
That's why I haven't put a grey line under the two letters in the middle of **said**.

Read each sentence. Match it to the correct picture.

She said her <u>ear</u> h<u>ur</u>t.

<u>Th</u>is sum is so h<u>ar</u>d.

He said it was wet.

Read the sentence. Circle the best picture for the sentence.

Tom said the p<u>oo</u>l
was t<u>oo</u> d<u>ee</u>p,
so he did not go in.

 That mark after the word **deep** is a comma. I like to take a little breath when I get to commas in sentences.

I can read captions and sentences
with the tricky words 'so' and 'said'.

Phonics — Reception Book 5

-nch and -nk

Say the word **pin**. If you add the sound **"ch"** to the end of **pin**, you get a new word: **pinch**.

Can you say the sounds in the word **pin** and the word **pinch**?

Read the caption, then **say** the sound on the card. Put them together. **Circle** the correct picture for the new word.

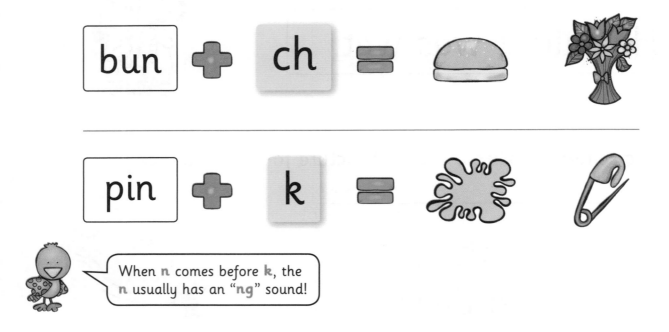

| bun | + | ch | = | (burger) (bunch of flowers) |

| pin | + | k | = | (splat) (safety pin) |

When **n** comes before **k**, the **n** usually has an **"ng"** sound!

Say the letter sounds, then blend them and say the word. **Circle** the correct picture.

wink

Read each caption. **Match** it to the correct picture.

think

munch

Say the words **sink** and **punch**. **Say** the sounds in each word. **Write** the letters in the word frames.

i   k   p

u   ch   n

n   s

Read the sentence. **Circle** the best picture for the sentence.

Hank left his lunch on a bench.

I can read and write words with
-nch and -nk at the end.

Writing Tricky Words 1

Some of the letters in tricky words have sounds you don't expect. Learn which letters are needed to write each word.

Practise until you can write them straight away.

Name the letters in the words **we**, **me**, **be**, **he** and **she**. Copy the letters into the special word frames.

we	me	be	he	she

Say: **She is in a sack.** Write this sentence in the word frames.

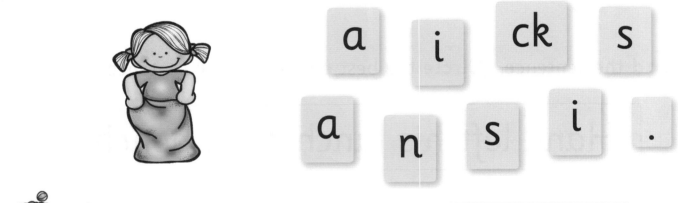

The word **she** is a tricky word. There are no letter cards to help you with this word!

She is the first word of the sentence, so it will need a capital letter at the start.

Say: **He runs with me.** **Write** this sentence in the word frames.

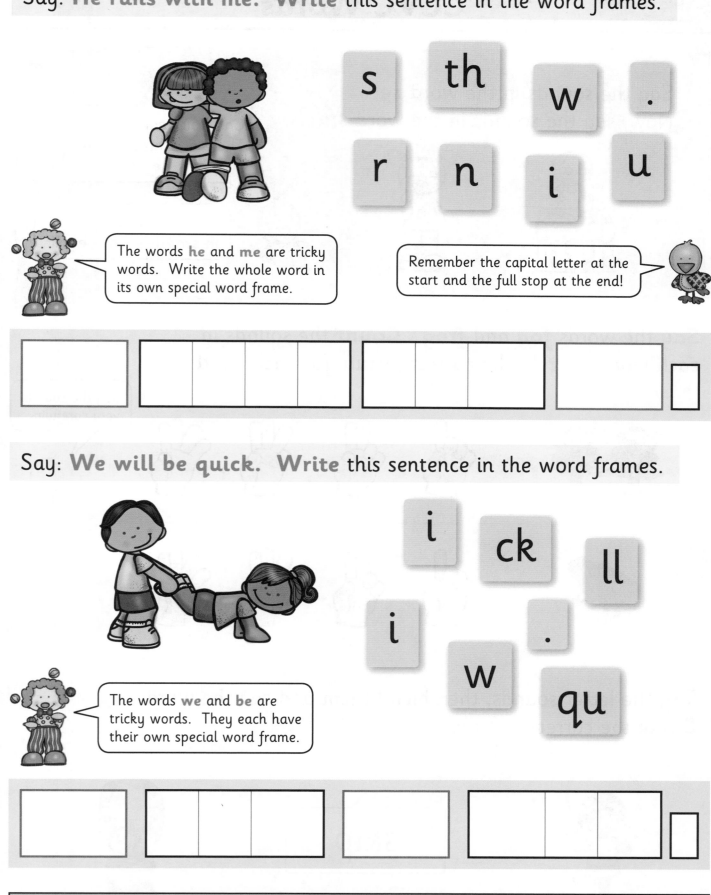

The words **he** and **me** are tricky words. Write the whole word in its own special word frame.

Remember the capital letter at the start and the full stop at the end!

Say: **We will be quick.** **Write** this sentence in the word frames.

The words **we** and **be** are tricky words. They each have their own special word frame.

I can write sentences that include the tricky words 'we', 'me', 'be', 'he' and 'she'.

Phonics — Reception Book 5

CCVC Words

Say the sounds in the word sell.
Now, say the sounds in the word smell.

Can you hear?
There are three sounds
in sell: s - e - ll.

There are four sounds
in smell: s - m - e - ll.

Say the words fog and frog. **Count** the sounds in each word. **Circle** the correct picture for each word.

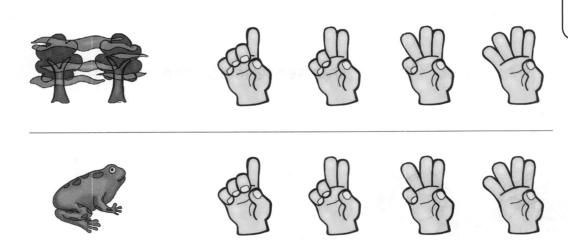

Say the sounds very carefully.

Say the letter sounds, then blend them and say the word. **Circle** the correct picture.

skip

Read each caption. **Match** it to the correct picture.

drum

clock

Say the words **flag** and **brick**. **Say** the sounds in each word. **Write** the letters in the word frames.

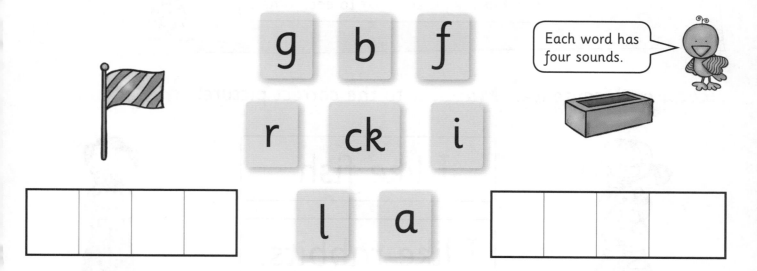

g   b   f

r   ck   i

l   a

Each word has four sounds.

Read the sentence. **Circle** the best picture for the sentence.

Stan and Fran spot a crab.

I can read and write words that have two consonants next to each other at the start.

Phonics — Reception Book 5

Reading Tricky Words 2

Let's learn some more tricky words.
These tricky words are like, have, some and come.

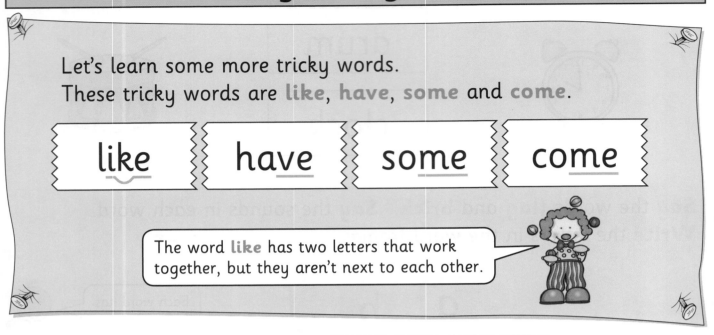

| like | have | some | come |

The word like has two letters that work together, but they aren't next to each other.

Read each sentence. **Match** it to the correct picture.

I like fish.

I like rabbits.

Look at the picture. **Read** the sentences.
Circle the correct sentence.

We have some sheep.

We have some cows.

Read each sentence. **Match** it to the correct picture.

I will come d<u>ow</u>n.

Some dogs are bla<u>ck</u>.

Can I come in?

Read the sentence. **Circle** the best picture for the sentence.

If you like buns, come and have some.

I can read captions and sentences with the
tricky words 'like', 'have', 'some' and 'come'.

shr- and thr-

Say the word **rug**. If you add the sound "**sh**"
to the start of **rug**, you get a new word: **shrug**.

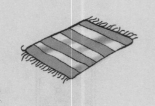

Can you say the sounds in the
word **rug** and the word **shrug**?

Say the sound on the card, then **read** the caption.
Put them together. **Circle** the correct picture for the new word.

sh ✚ red =

th ✚ ra**sh** =

Read each sentence. **Match** it to the correct picture.

It is a <u>thr</u>i<u>ll</u>.

It is <u>too</u> <u>shr</u>i<u>ll</u>.

I can read words with shr- and thr- at the start.

CCCVC Words

Let's think about words with even more sounds.
Count the sounds in the word spring.

Wow! There are five sounds in spring: s - p - r - i - ng.

Read each caption. **Match** it to the correct picture.

scrub

strong

Read the caption. **Circle** the best picture for the caption.

a scrap of string

I can read words with three consonants
next to each other at the start.

Writing Tricky Words 2

Let's learn to spell a few more tricky words. Look carefully at the letters needed for each word.

Say the letter names, one after the other.

Name the letters in the words **was** and **you**.
Copy the letters into the special word frames.

| was | you |

Practise until you can write these words straight away.

Say: **This is for you.** **Write** the sentence in the word frames.

s   or   .   i

s   Th   i   f

The word **you** has its own special word frame. Write the whole word in this frame.

Two children decided to dress up.
Say: **Jen was a bee.** **Write** this sentence in the word frames.

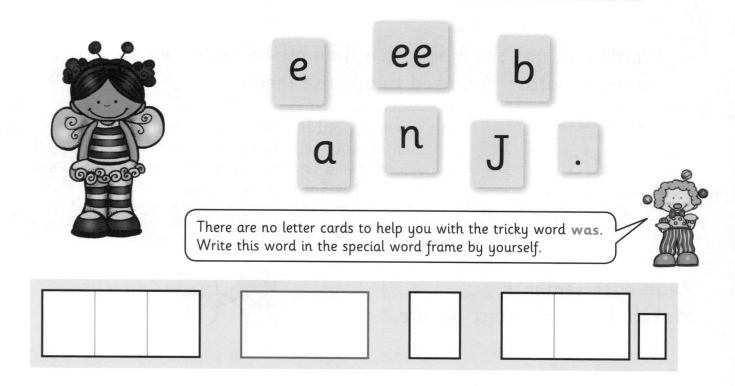

There are no letter cards to help you with the tricky word **was**. Write this word in the special word frame by yourself.

Say: **Gus was a cat.** **Write** this sentence in the word frames.

There's that tricky word **was** again!

Have you remembered to put a full stop at the end?

I can write sentences that include the tricky words 'was' and 'you'.

Phonics — Reception Book 5

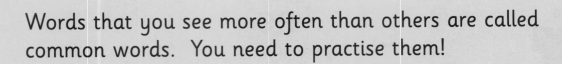

Common Words

Words that you see more often than others are called common words. You need to practise them!

it's

This common word **it's** has a special mark called an apostrophe. The word is short for two words: **it** and **is**. The apostrophe shows where the **i** of **is** has been missed out.

Read each sentence.
Match it to the correct picture.

Look out for the word **it's**!

It's a du<u>ck</u>.

It's an ant.

Look at the picture. **Read** the captions.
Circle the correct caption.

Watch out for some tricky words on these pages!

a box of sna<u>ck</u>s

a box but no sna<u>ck</u>s

Read each sentence. **Match** it to the correct picture.

This dog can beg.

I had a go at it.

Look at that jet.

Read the sentences. **Circle** the best picture for these sentences.

He got on it with me.
We went up and down.

I can read captions and sentences with common words.

Phonics — Reception Book 5

CCVCC Words

Let's look at some more words that have five sounds.

I think you're going to enjoy this!

Say the words **ram**, **ramp** and **cramp**.
Count the sounds in each word.
Circle the correct picture.

Have you ever had cramp?

Say the letter sounds, then blend them and say the word.
Circle the correct picture.

trunk

Read each caption. **Match** it to the correct picture.

stump

skunk

Say the words **drink** and **twist**. **Say** the sounds in each word. **Write** the letters in the word frames.

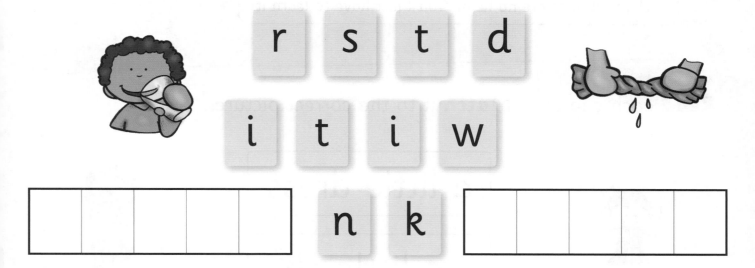

Read the sentence. **Circle** the best picture for the sentence.

Frank can stamp in the crisp frost.

I can read and write words that have two consonants next to each other at each end.

Reading Tricky Words 3

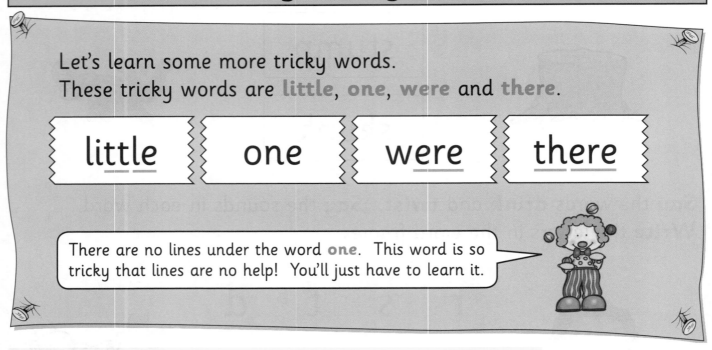

Let's learn some more tricky words.
These tricky words are little, one, were and there.

little one were there

There are no lines under the word one. This word is so tricky that lines are no help! You'll just have to learn it.

Read each caption. **Match** it to the correct picture.

a little dress

a little elf

Look at the picture. **Read** the captions.
Circle the correct caption.

one fish in a tank

seven fish in a tank

Read each sentence. **Match** it to the correct picture.

One of the bloc<u>ck</u>s is red.

We were at the golf club.

I will get there next.

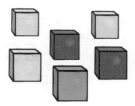

Read the sentence. **Circle** the best picture for the sentence.

There were six big gifts and a little one.

I can read captions and sentences with the tricky words 'little', 'one', 'were' and 'there'.

Phonics — Reception Book 5

Adding Endings

Adding letters to the end of a word makes other words!

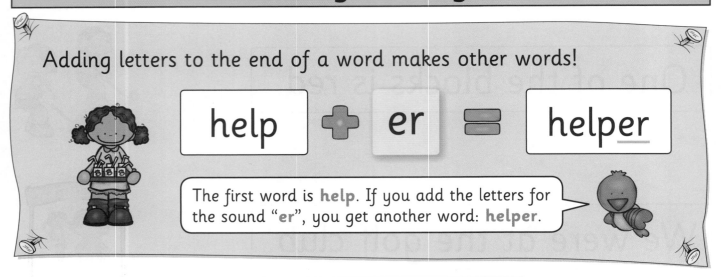

help ➕ er 🟰 help<u>er</u>

The first word is **help**. If you add the letters for the sound "**er**", you get another word: **helper**.

Read the caption, then say the sound on the card.
Put them together, then **circle** the correct picture.

camp ➕ er 🟰 camp<u>er</u>

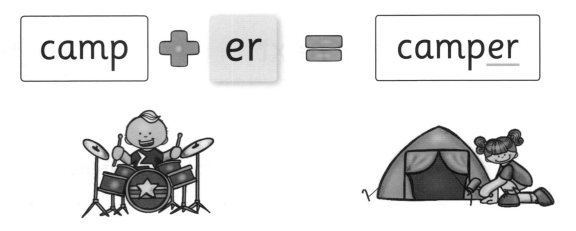

Read the captions. **Think** about how these chairs might feel.
Match each caption to the best picture.

soft   sof<u>t</u>er   softest

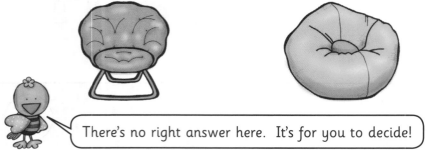

There's no right answer here. It's for you to decide!

Read the captions below each picture.
Circle the best caption for that picture.

Sometimes the last letter is doubled when endings are added.

| standing | resting | jumping |

| sitting | thinking | sulking |

Read the sentence. Circle the best picture for the sentence.

The farmer is selling his freshest corn.

I can read words that have endings added.

Writing Tricky Words 3

It's time to learn to write some more tricky words.

Tricky words are useful words to know. You'll use them a lot!

Name the letters in the words **they**, **all** and **are**. **Copy** the letters into the special word frames.

they   all   are

These tricky words might take a bit of practice!

Say: **Off they go.** **Write** this sentence in the word frames.

 ff   o   .

*The words **they** and **go** are both tricky words. There are no letter cards to help you with these words!*

*Do you remember how to spell the tricky word **go**?*

Say: **They are up high.** **Write** this sentence in the word frames.

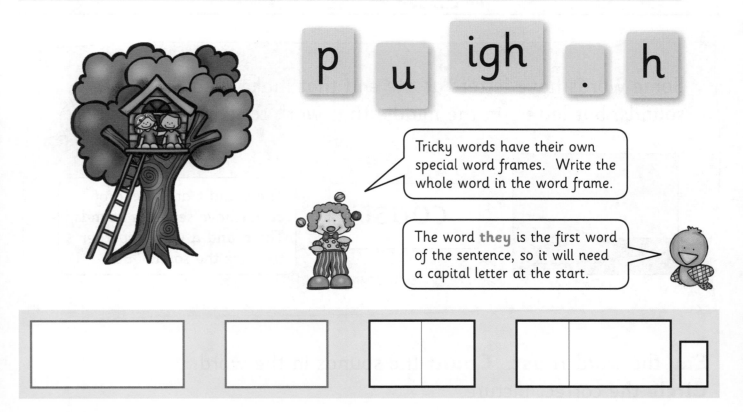

p u igh . h

Tricky words have their own special word frames. Write the whole word in the word frame.

The word **they** is the first word of the sentence, so it will need a capital letter at the start.

Say: **They all had fun.** **Write** this sentence in the word frames.

d a n .

u h f

Don't forget the full stop at the end of the sentence.

I can write sentences that include the tricky words 'they', 'all' and 'are'.

C<u>VV</u>CC Words

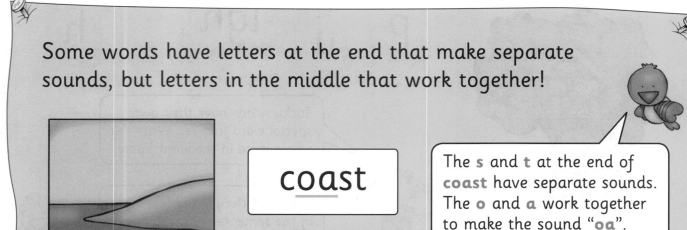

Some words have letters at the end that make separate sounds, but letters in the middle that work together!

coast

The **s** and **t** at the end of **coast** have separate sounds. The **o** and **a** work together to make the sound "**oa**".

Say the word **roost**. **Count** the sounds in the word.
Circle the correct picture.

When birds settle down for a sleep or a rest, they roost.

roo<u>s</u>t

Say the letter sounds, then blend them and say the word.
Circle the correct picture.

p<u>ai</u>nt

Phonics — Reception Book 5

Read each caption. **Match** it to the correct picture.

toast

point

Say the words **hoist** and **boost**. **Say** the sounds in each word.
Write the letters in the word frames.

| h | b | t |

| s | t | oo |

| s | oi |

| | | | |

| | | | |

Read the sentence. **Circle** the best picture for the sentence.

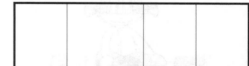
The r<u>oa</u>st is m<u>oi</u>st, not b<u>ur</u>nt.

I can read and write words that have two consonants
at the end and a vowel digraph in the middle.

Reading Tricky Words 4

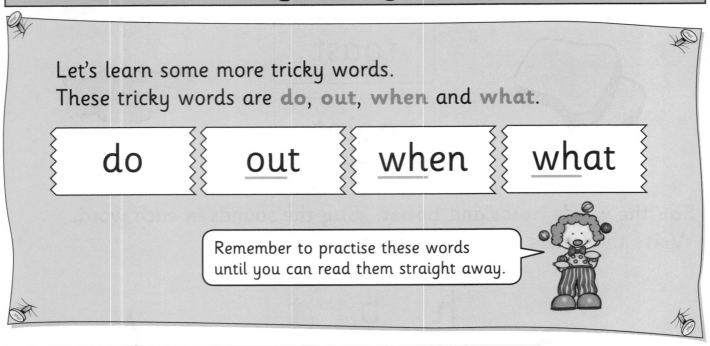

Let's learn some more tricky words.
These tricky words are do, out, when and what.

| do | out | when | what |

Remember to practise these words until you can read them straight away.

Read each caption. **Match** it to the correct picture.

cut out

s<u>or</u>t out

Look at the picture. **Read** the sentences.
Circle the correct sentence.

Do you like plums?

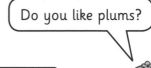

I do not like plums.

I do like plums.

Read each sentence. Match it to the correct picture.

I am glad when it r<u>ai</u>ns.

Anna can do the splits.

I s<u>ee</u> what is in the j<u>ar</u>.

Read the sentences. Circle the best picture for these sentences.

<u>Th</u>is is what Fred and Sa<u>sh</u>a do when it's hot. They <u>ch</u>i<u>ll</u> out.

I can read captions and sentences with the tricky words 'do', 'out', 'when' and 'what'.

Phonics — Reception Book 5

CCVVC Words

Let's think about words with letters at the start that make separate sounds but letters in the middle that work together.

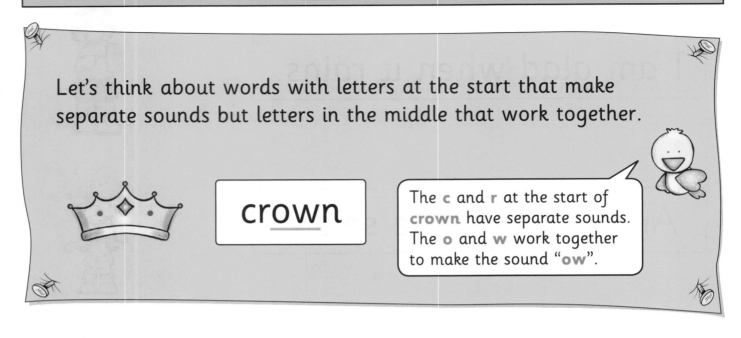

crown

The **c** and **r** at the start of **crown** have separate sounds. The **o** and **w** work together to make the sound "**ow**".

Say the word **spoon**. **Count** the sounds in the word.
Circle the correct picture for the number of sounds.

spoon

Say the letter sounds, then blend them and say the word.
Circle the correct picture.

sweet

Read each caption. **Match** it to the correct picture.

float

sleep

Say the words **train** and **crowd**. **Say** the sounds in each word.
Write the letters in the word frames.

r c n

t d ow

r ai

Read the sentence. **Circle** the best picture for the sentence.

The cl<u>ow</u>n st<u>oo</u>d on a gr<u>ee</u>n st<u>ar</u>.

I can read and write words that have two consonants
at the start and a vowel digraph in the middle.

Phonics — Reception Book 5

Questions and Answers

Questions ask you something. They need answers.

Do bees buzz?

You can tell when a sentence is a question. It has a special mark, called a question mark, at the end.

Read these questions. They're all about you! If the answer is yes, put a **tick** (✓) in the box. If the answer is no, put a **cross** (X).

Do you like carrots?

Do you like swimming?

Read the question, then **read** the two possible answers. **Circle** the correct answer.

When is it dark?

at noon

at night

The word **noon** means twelve o'clock in the middle of the day.

Read each question. **Circle** the correct answer.

What is milk?

a drink

a c<u>ar</u>

What is a lamp?

a bed

a <u>light</u>

Read each question. **Match** it to the correct answer.

Do camels have humps?

never

When will <u>sh</u>ar<u>k</u>s clap?

six

What is <u>three</u> plus <u>three</u>?

yes

  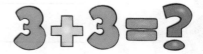

I can read questions and answer them.

Longer Words

Most of the words you've been learning have been short words. Let's read some longer words now.

sisters

> It's just like reading shorter words. Say the letter sounds, then blend them and say the word. This word says **sisters**.

Say the letter sounds, then blend them and say the word.
Circle the correct picture.

sandwich

Read each caption. **Match** it to the correct picture.

in the garden

at the market

Phonics — Reception Book 5

Read each caption. **Match** it to the correct picture.

flowers for a present

shampoo near a towel

thunder and lightning

 Don't be put off by the long words. Just say the sounds in the word, then blend them.

Read the sentence. **Circle** the best picture for the sentence.

The children are carving a pumpkin.

I can read longer words.

© CGP — Not to be photocopied

Phonics — Reception Book 5

Writing Tricky Words 4

Let's learn to spell two more tricky words.

We'll also practise some of the other tricky words you know.

Name the letters in the words **my** and **her**.
Copy the letters into the special word frames.

my

her

Practise until you can write these words straight away.

Say: **I go in my boat.** **Write** this sentence in the word frames.

n oa i b t .

There are three tricky words in this sentence. Two of them are words that you learned earlier.

Tricky words have their own special word frames. Write the whole word in the word frame.

Say: **She has her bag.** **Write** this sentence in the word frames.

Just two tricky words in this sentence. One is a word you learned earlier.

Remember that the first word of the sentence needs a capital letter at the start.

Say: **My mum hugs her.** **Write** this sentence in the word frames.

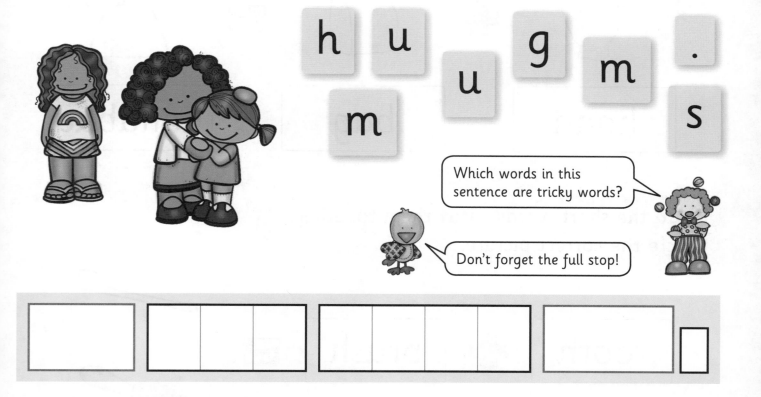

Which words in this sentence are tricky words?

Don't forget the full stop!

I can write sentences that include the tricky words 'my' and 'her'.

Phonics — Reception Book 5

Compound Words

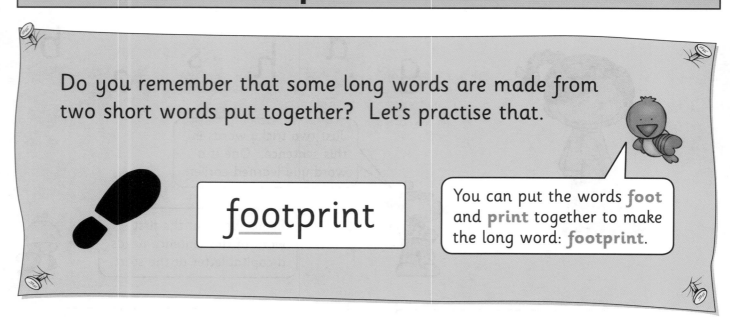

Do you remember that some long words are made from two short words put together? Let's practise that.

footprint

You can put the words **foot** and **print** together to make the long word: **footprint**.

Read the short words. Put them together and **read** the long word. **Colour** the pictures.

hand + bag = handbag

Read the short words. **Put** them together. **Circle** the correct picture.

tooth + brush =

Read each caption.
Match it to the correct picture.

lunchbox

lipstick

Say the long word **sandpit**. Say the two short words you hear.
Say the sounds. Write the letters in the word frame.

a   d   n   i

t   s   p

It's one long word, so there's one long word frame!

Read the sentence. Circle the best picture for the sentence.

I did a handstand in the spotlight.

I can read and write long words that are made up of two short words.

Grand Finale

The name of each animal is on a sign next to the food it eats.
Match the animals to their dinner!

There are some things missing from this picture.
Read the caption. **Complete** the picture, then colour it.

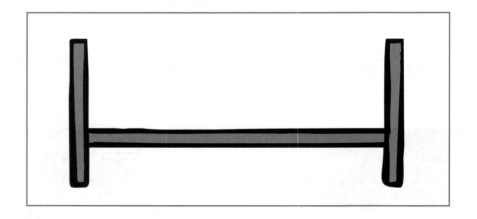

a clo<u>ck</u> and a lamp on a <u>sh</u>elf

Mark the answers on this quiz paper. If the answer is correct, put a **tick** (✓) in the box. If the answer is wrong, put a **cross** (X).

1. Do cats have f<u>ur</u>?
   Yes, they do. ☐

2. What is a st<u>ar</u>?
   It's an animal. ☐

3. When do <u>ch</u>ildren sl<u>ee</u>p?
   They sl<u>ee</u>p at n<u>igh</u>t. ☐

Read the captions on each puzzle piece. Put the words together.
Match the puzzle piece to the picture of the new word.

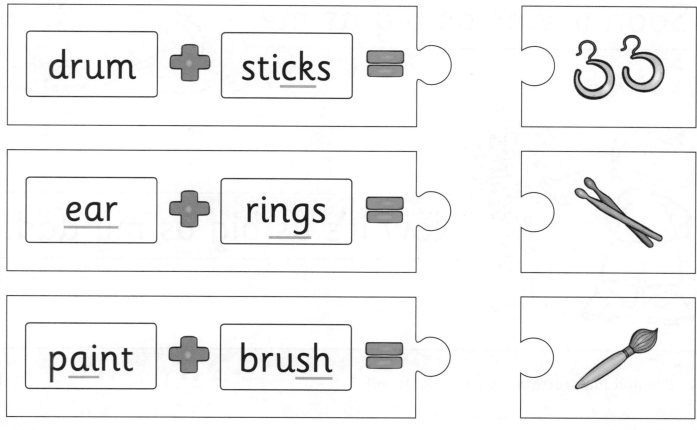

Read the story, then **colour** the pictures.

It was just a little s<u>ee</u>d.

Th<u>en</u> there was a gr<u>een</u> sh<u>oo</u>t.

S<u>oo</u>n it was as big as me.

N<u>ow</u> it's as big as my dad.

I've had fun practising what I've learned!

EROW511